D1321473

COVENTRY LIBRARIES

PS130553 Disk 4

**Please return this book on or before
the last date stamped below.**

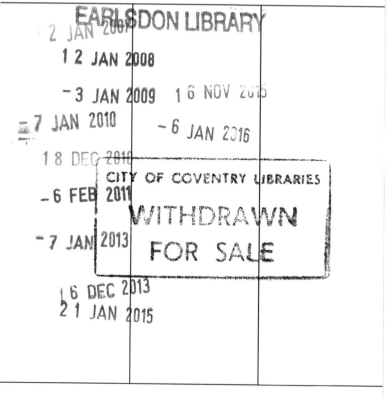

EARLSDON LIBRARY

2 JAN 2007

1 2 JAN 2008

-3 JAN 2009   1 6 NOV 2015

-7 JAN 2010   -6 JAN 2016

1 8 DEC 2010

-6 FEB 2011

-7 JAN 2013

CITY OF COVENTRY LIBRARIES

WITHDRAWN
FOR SALE

1 6 DEC 2013
2 1 JAN 2015

To renew this book take it to any of
the City Libraries before
the date due for return.

Coventry City Council

To Leah Morris, for being such an inspiration, MBH & KL
To my nieces, Tilly, Hannah and Ellie, MBH
To Renate, KL

Leah's Christmas Story

Margaret Bateson-Hill

Karin Littlewood

COVENTRY CITY LIBRARIES	
PETERS	09-Nov-06
JF	£9.99
1/12/06	

LION
CHILDREN'S

Bethlehem was always a busy city but tonight it was full to overflowing with travellers who had returned to the city of their birth. Everyone was to be registered in the census ordered by the Roman emperor, Augustus.

The city was far too crowded for an innkeeper's daughter trying to make her way home with food for the hungry guests. Twice already the basket had been knocked from Leah's hands.

As she turned the corner that led to her father's inn, Leah's heart
sank. The street was full of people searching for somewhere to stay.
   Leah started to make her way through the crowds when, suddenly,
she stopped quite still. A great silver star was shining directly above
her home. It was so beautiful that she could only gaze upwards,
amazed by its shining splendour…

She didn't see the donkey until she felt a sharp kick on her knee!

A man called, "Look out!" as Leah fell down with a bump and the contents of her basket went flying across the street. Instead of the silver glory of the star, she could only see the hard earth and the hooves of the donkey trampling through her vegetables. Leah could feel a bruise swelling up on her knee. The pain brought tears to her eyes.

At that moment, her father came running out from the inn.

"What took you so long? Pick everything up, then come and help. I'm rushed off my feet."

Leah wiped her eyes on her sleeve. There was no point in feeling sorry for herself. She knew her father wasn't really cross, just too busy.

A strong pair of arms lifted her back onto her feet and she heard a woman's voice asking if she was all right. The woman was sitting on the donkey. She was young and very pregnant.

As Leah picked up the vegetables, she heard the woman say
"Joseph, the baby is coming! What are we going to do?"

Leah didn't stop to think.

"If it's a baby, you'll need Susanna. She knows everything!"
Leah ran across the street calling, "Susanna, come quickly,
a baby's being born."

Susanna came hurrying out and the man turned to her with
desperation on his face.

"But we've nowhere to stay. Everywhere is full."

Then a deep voice called out from the doorway of the inn.
"There's no room in here, but I have got a stable. It's not much,
but at least it'll be warm and dry, and quiet."

Leah looked over to her father. She knew the birth of every baby
reminded him of the night she'd been born. She smiled at him,
then taking the donkey's reins, she led the way to the stable.

After the growing coldness and dark outside, the stable was warm and comforting. Susanna immediately took charge.

"Leah, get another light and some blankets for Mary."

Leah rushed around, helping as best she could. Then suddenly, she realized there was no cradle for the baby, so she filled the animals' feed box with new hay and covered it with a little blanket of her own.

She couldn't think of anything else to do, so she sat down in a corner of the stable hoping that she wouldn't be sent away before the baby came. Oh, how long did babies take to be born?

Leah peeped out of her corner at Mary. Soon she would be a mother. She was walking around the stable, holding tightly to Joseph and Susanna.

"Just take things slowly," advised Susanna. "It could be a long night."

Leah wondered how many mothers Susanna had helped. Her father had told her that it was Susanna who had saved Leah's life the night she was born… though her mother had died…

Leah lay back and stared up at the roof of the stable. Through a small hole, she realized she could see the star. It was glowing brightly, as though it were watching over the stable. As she lay in the warm, sweet-smelling hay, her thoughts began to drift and she wondered if her own mother ever watched over her from somewhere high above…

Leah opened her eyes. She could hear voices laughing and a baby was crying. The baby was already here!

Leah crept slowly out of her dark corner into the soft golden light of the lamp. Mary was cradling her newborn son with such love and tenderness that Leah suddenly felt incredibly shy.

Then Susanna caught sight of her and laughed.

"What happened to my little helper? I thought you were impatient to help me bring this little boy into the world. Well, come and see him. His name is Jesus."

Leah could only gaze in wonder at the baby. He was so small and perfect and lovely, snuggled in his mother's arms, that she wanted to cry!

Then there was a quiet knock at the stable door and in came Leah's father. He looked puzzled.

"There are some shepherds outside and they want to see the baby." he said. He stopped for a moment as if he could barely believe the next words he was going to say.

"They say they were sent by angels."

Slowly the shepherds crowded into the stable. Their faces mirrored the long, hard seasons spent in the open, but their eyes shone with a fierce joy. In a trembling voice, the oldest one spoke of the heavenly vision they had seen, "They told us he was the Christ… the messiah, the king we have been waiting for."

Leah stared at the shepherd in disbelief. "But then Jesus would live in a palace, not in my stable."

"Maybe," replied the old shepherd, "but remember, even great King David himself was once a shepherd boy in the very fields we work in!"

Was Jesus really a king?

Over the next few days, Leah could think of nothing else. Finally, she just had to ask the only person who might know.

"Is Jesus a special baby, like the shepherds said?"

Mary smiled at Leah's questioning face.

"Every baby is special," she replied, "but I believe that Jesus is the chosen one of God. I do not know what that will mean, but I believe that God will look after him, just as he did by bringing us to this stable.

"Of course, he couldn't have done that without you, Leah."

"Me!" said Leah.

"God often chooses little people to do great things for him," Mary replied softly.

That night, as she was getting ready for bed, Leah saw the star shining so brightly she thought the whole world must know that God had sent Jesus to her stable. Wouldn't everyone be so happy!

She crept closer to the window, wanting to catch one last glimpse of the star's silver brightness before she went to sleep – only to find herself looking at three travellers, richly dressed in silken robes.

Leah called to her father, then ran to open the inn door. One of the travellers came and knelt down so close to her that she could smell the perfume of the oils that scented his skin. And when he spoke, the sound of his voice made her think of faraway places.

"We are learned scholars who have journeyed for many days, following the star you see shining above you. But now we are here, we find that the star shines above a simple stable. Tell us we have not journeyed in vain. Is this the place we are seeking? Is the Christ child within?"

"Yes," whispered Leah, "he's here." The three travellers entered the stable and when they saw the baby and his mother, they fell to their knees and each one brought out a great treasure, gifts for a king; gold, frankincense and myrrh.

"But if you have followed the star," thought Leah, "who else will be coming…"

Leah woke up just before dawn. It was dark. She didn't need to look out of the window to know that the silver star was gone. But had Jesus gone too?

Leah ran to the stable and stood outside waiting, listening, trembling…

People were moving inside. They were still there! Softly, she pushed open the door. She could see her blankets folded in a tidy pile in the corner of the stable. She stood in the doorway and whispered, "Are you going away?"

"Yes," Mary sighed, "Jesus is in danger. Joseph had a dream… King Herod's soldiers are coming."

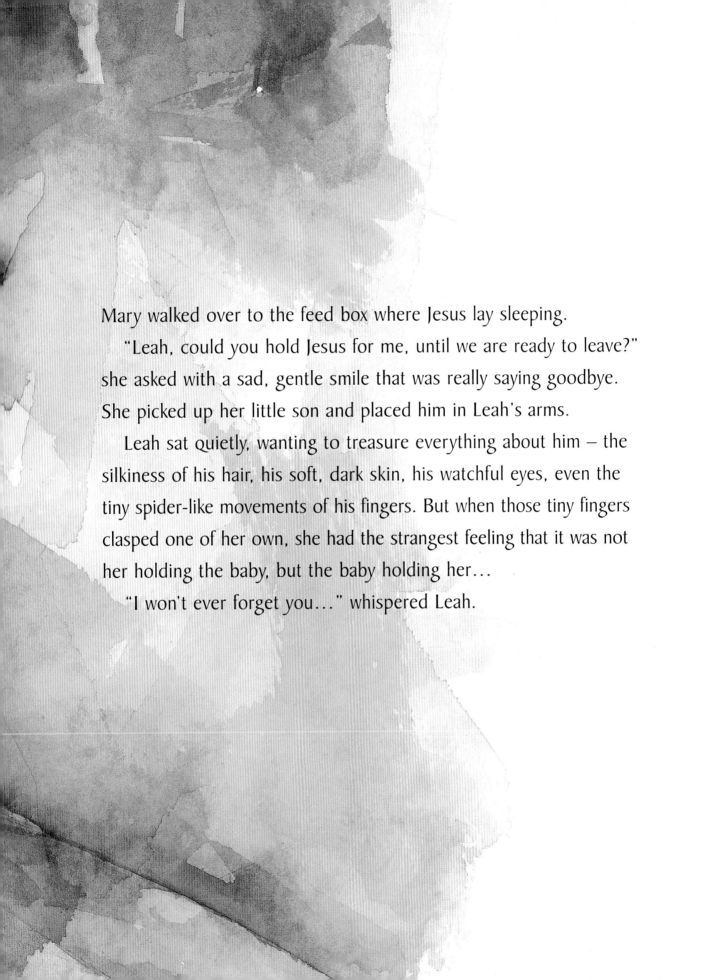

Mary walked over to the feed box where Jesus lay sleeping.

"Leah, could you hold Jesus for me, until we are ready to leave?" she asked with a sad, gentle smile that was really saying goodbye. She picked up her little son and placed him in Leah's arms.

Leah sat quietly, wanting to treasure everything about him – the silkiness of his hair, his soft, dark skin, his watchful eyes, even the tiny spider-like movements of his fingers. But when those tiny fingers clasped one of her own, she had the strangest feeling that it was not her holding the baby, but the baby holding her…

"I won't ever forget you…" whispered Leah.

Text © 2006 Margaret Bateson-Hill
Illustrations © 2006 Karin Littlewood
Leah's Christmas Story © 2006 2AM Publishing

A Lion Children's Book
an imprint of
Lion Hudson plc
Mayfield House, 256 Banbury Road,
Oxford OX2 7DH, England
www.lionhudson.com
ISBN-13: 978-0-7459-4997-0
ISBN-10: 0-7459-4997-5 (hardback)
ISBN-13: 978-0-7459-4998-7
ISBN-10: 0-7459-4998-3 (paperback)

Published under licence from 2AM Publishing

First edition 2006
10 9 8 7 6 5 4 3 2 1 0

All rights reserved

A catalogue record for this book is available
from the British Library

Typeset in 16/24 BakerSignet BT
Printed and bound in China